CAHIER D'EXERCICES

FRENCH IS FUN

BOOK 1 **2ND EDITION**

Gail Stein

Foreign Language Department
Martin Van Buren High School
New York City

Heywood Wald, PhD

Former Assistant Principal
Foreign Language Department
Martin Van Buren High School
New York City

When ordering this book, please specify *either* **R 537 A**
or CAHIER, FRENCH IS FUN, BOOK 1

AMSCO SCHOOL PUBLICATIONS, INC.
315 Hudson Street/New York, N.Y. 10013

Preface

This CAHIER D'EXERCICES supplements the practice materials in FRENCH IS FUN, BOOK 1, SECOND EDITION. The vocabulary and structural elements are closely coordinated with parallel chapters in the textbook.

While some exercises use techniques similar to those in the basal text, others extend the range of the materials. The workbook format provides opportunity for writing practice and intensive homework.

The pages are perforated to permit the collection of home or class assignments.

ISBN 0-87720-025-4

Copyright © 1991 by Amsco School Publications, Inc.

Printed in the United States of America

——— Leçon 1 ———————

A. What can you see in Marie-Claire's room besides the furniture?

1. _____   6. _____

2. _____   7. _____

3. _____   8. _____

4. _____   9. _____

5. _____   10. _____

B. Today you went to see a movie with a friend. List four adjectives that describe the movie:

1. _____   3. _____

2. _____   4. _____

C. The Maréchals are tourists in your city. Identify the places they saw:

1. _____

2. _____

3. _____

4. _____

5. _____

6. _____

7. _____

8. _____

9. _____   **10.** _____

D. Identify what you like (**J'aime**) or don't like (**Je n'aime pas**) by placing **le**, **la**, or **l'** before the nouns listed below:

classe	musique rock	école
cinéma	leçon	professeur
télévision	danse	sport
docteur		

1. _____

2. _____

3. _____

4. _____

5. _____

6. _____

7. _____

8. _____

9. _____

10. _____

E. **Oui** (*Yes*) **ou Non** (*No*). If the statement is true, write **vrai**. If it is false, write **faux**:

1. Le docteur est intelligent. _____

2. L'éléphant est rouge. _____

3. Le président est populaire. _____

4. La musique rock est moderne. _____

5. Le professeur de français est blond. _____

F. Give your opinion of each item by choosing from the list of adjectives given:

         intelligent   nécessaire   confortable
         excellent   délicieux   américain
         populaire   horrible   immense
         élégant

1. Le fruit est _____.

2. Le menu est _____.

3. Le pull-over est _____.

4. L'accident est _____.

5. Le programme est _____.

6. L'appartement est _____.

7. L'acteur est _____.

8. Le vocabulaire est _____.

9. Le président est _____.

10. L'éléphant est _____.

___ Leçon 2 _____

A. Can you identify Marc Dupont's relatives?

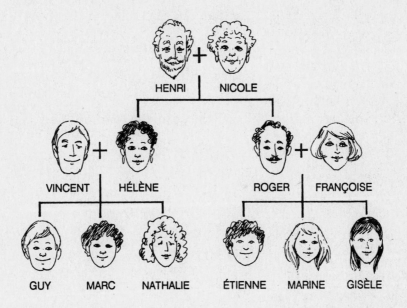

1. Vincent est _____.

2. Henri est _____.

3. Nicole est _____.

4. Guy est _____.

5. Hélène est _____.

6. Françoise est _____.

7. Roger est _____.

8. Gisèle est _____.

9. Étienne est _____.

10. Nathalie est _____.

B. List and identify five members of a friend's family:

EXAMPLE: Jacques est le père.

1. _____

2. _____

3. _____

4. _____

5. _____

C. Look at this picture and identify all those at the reunion (Use as many plurals as possible.):

1. _____   5. _____

2. _____   6. _____

3. _____   7. _____

4. _____   8. _____

D. Roland works at the flea market. He has to change all the signs to show that more than one of each item is being sold. Write the changes that he will have to make:

EXAMPLE: la table   les tables

1. la blouse   _____

2. l'animal   _____

3. l'automobile _____

4. la radio   _____

5. le fruit   _____

6. le disque   _____

7. le journal   _____

8. le stylo   _____

9. le bureau   _____

10. le pull-over _____

11. la bicyclette _____

12. le téléphone _____

13. la guitare   _____

14. la télévision _____

E. Look at each picture and tell how you feel about the thing(s) depicted:

J'adore   Je n'aime pas
J'aime   Je déteste

EXAMPLES:

J'aime les chats.

Je n'aime pas les chiens.

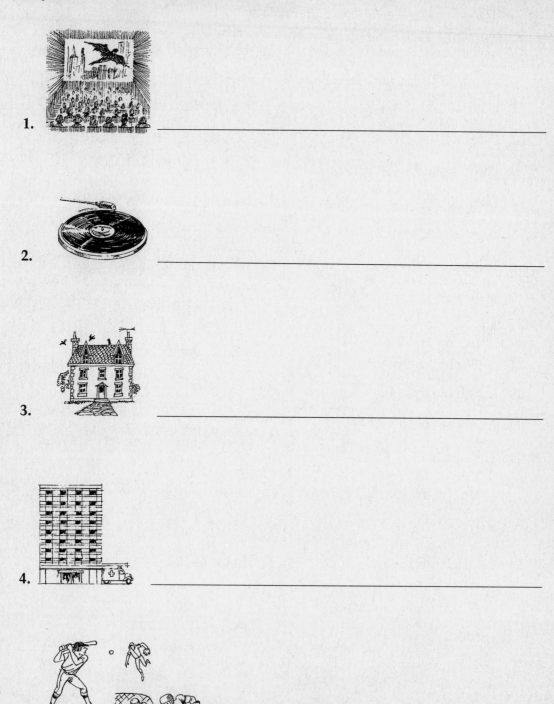

1. _____

2. _____

3. _____

4. _____

5. _____

6. _____

7. _____

8. _____

9. _____

10. _____

11. _____

12. _____

13. _____

14. _____

15. _____

F. Your French pen pal plans to come to visit you. Write him/her a note in French about your family:

_____

_____

_____

_____

____ Leçon 3 _____

A. It is Pierre's first day of school. Identify the people and objects that he is looking at:

EXAMPLE: Il regarde le bureau.

1. _____

2. _____

3. _____

4. _____

5. _____

6. _____

7. _____

8. _____

9. _____

10. _____

11. _____

12. _____

B. Describe the subjects using one of the following adjectives:

drôle	grand
intéressant	noir
moderne	difficile
sympathique	rouge

1. L'élève est _____.

2. Le dictionnaire est _____.

3. Le professeur est _____.

4. Le livre est _____.

5. Le tableau est _____.

6. L'exercice est _____.

7. Le bureau est _____.

8. Le crayon est _____.

C. Write a list of six things you always have in your school bag:

1. _____   4. _____

2. _____   5. _____

3. _____   6. _____

D. Supply the correct indefinite article (**un**, **une**, or **des**) as you identify who or what you see while walking in the city:

1. _____ animaux   12. _____ docteurs

2. _____ restaurant   13. _____ parc

3. _____ artistes   14. _____ bicyclettes

4. _____ train   15. _____ cathédrale

5. _____ bureau   16. _____ cafés

6. _____ maison   17. _____ hôtel

7. _____ accident   18. _____ bébés

8. _____ boutique   19. _____ cinéma

9. _____ jardins   20. _____ vendeurs

10. _____ appartements   21. _____ famille

11. _____ hôpital   22. _____ automobiles

E. There are 16 school-related items hidden in the puzzle. Circle the words from left to right, right to left, up or down, or diagonally:

```
D   C   B   U   A   C   B   U   R   E   A   U

E   I   Y   R   C   R   A   Y   O   N   N   O

E   L   C   E   F   P   R   H   R   C   E   E

É   Y   S   T   T   E   D   E   I   R   L   C

L   T   O   T   I   D   L   P   T   E   E   T

È   V   U   P   Y   O   R   Ê   A   B   R   A

V   D   A   D   C   L   N   O   N   L   E   B

E   P   P   É   I   E   O   N   A   I   B   L

U   B   V   O   F   A   G   E   A   F   E   E

L   L   I   V   R   E   N   R   T   I   R   A

R   È   G   L   E   T   C   T   V   E   R   U

A   R   U   E   S   S   E   F   O   R   P   E
```

F. Janine is looking in an old trunk in the attic. Write what she finds:

EXAMPLE: Elle trouve (*She finds*) une télévision.

1. _____

2. _____

3. _____

4. _____

5. _____

6. _____

7. _____

8. _____

9. _____

10. _____

11. _____

12. _____

13. _____

14. _____

15. _____

_____ Leçon 4 _____

A. Match the verb with the noun that could be used to describe what happened at Lucien's party. Write the matching letters in the space provided:

1. goûter _____
2. regarder _____
3. écouter _____
4. chanter _____
5. danser _____
6. jouer _____
7. gagner _____
8. parler _____

a. des disques
b. le disco
c. un prix (*a prize*)
d. le dessert
e. «Joyeux anniversaire» (*Happy Birthday*)
f. français
g. dans le jardin
h. un film

B. Write the pronoun you would use (**tu** or **vous**) if you were speaking to these people:

1. un enfant _____
2. le père de Richard _____
3. Valérie et André _____
4. le président _____
5. Georges _____
6. ta (*your*) sœur _____

C. Write the pronoun you could use to substitute for each noun:

1. Hélène _____
2. Michel et Éric _____

3. Lisette et Jacques   _____

4. Mme Restaud   _____

5. Paul   _____

6. les docteurs   _____

7. le livre   _____

8. la porte et la fenêtre   _____

9. la craie   _____

10. les dictionnaires   _____

D. Fill in the correct form of a verb that makes sense in the sentence, choosing from the following list:

aimer	fermer	penser
arriver	habiter	préparer
donner	inviter	trouver
entrer		

1. Tu _____ dans la classe.

2. Le professeur _____ la fenêtre.

3. René _____ le dictionnaire à Roland.

4. Georgette _____ beaucoup Paul.

5. Les élèves _____ à l'école.

6. Alain _____ ses (his) amis à une surprise-partie.

7. J'_____ New York.

8. Nous _____ la mousse.

9. Vous _____ le livre.

10. Elles _____ à (about) l'examen.

E. Write what these people do in their spare time:

      EXAMPLE: Je/écouter la radio.
               J'écoute la radio.

1. André/travailler sur son (*his*) auto

   _____

2. Je/regarder la télévision

   _____

3. Alice et Sylvie/écouter des disques

   _____

4. Tu/préparer un dessert délicieux

   _____

5. Ils/chanter

   _____

6. Nous/jouer au football

   _____

7. Vous/danser à la discothèque

   _____

8. Elles/marcher dans le parc

   _____

9. Il/penser à son amie

   _____

10. Elle/parler au téléphone

   _____

F. Write a list of five things you do in your spare time:

1. _____

2. _____

3. _____

4. _____

5. _____

G. Your friend Marie tells you what she does and asks if you do the same. Give a negative answer to her questions:

EXAMPLE: Je joue au tennis. Et toi (*and you*)?
Je ne joue pas au tennis.

1. J'habite un appartement. Et toi?

_____

2. J'aime le golf. Et toi?

_____

3. J'arrive à l'école en retard (*late*). Et toi?

_____

4. Je gagne beaucoup d'argent (*money*). Et toi?

_____

5. Je travaille après (*after*) l'école. Et toi?

_____

6. Je parle italien. Et toi?

_____

H. Write what some students in your class don't do:

EXAMPLE: Jean/penser à l'école
Jean ne pense pas à l'école.

1. André/danser bien

_____

2. les filles/chanter beaucoup

_____

3. nous/inviter le professeur au cinéma

_____

4. Luc et Paul/parler souvent au téléphone

_____

5. Anne/jouer au tennis

_____

6. je/préparer le dîner

_____

7. elle/travailler dur (*hard*)

_____

8. tu/écouter la musique rock

_____

9. vous/regarder les programmes de sport

_____

10. les garçons/marcher dans le parc

_____

I. Change all the statements to questions using **Est-ce que**?

1. Ils cherchent un hôtel confortable.

_____

2. Tu joues bien au base-ball.

_____

3. Elles invitent les garçons.

_____

4. Vous arrivez en France avec Marie.

_____

5. Tu prépares un dîner délicieux.

_____

6. Ils travaillent dans la boutique.

_____

7. Elles trouvent un bon (_good_) restaurant.

_____

8. Vous gagnez le match.

_____

J. You can't believe your ears when your friend tells you about her cousins. Question her using inversion:

EXAMPLE: Il chante beaucoup.
　　　　　Chante-t-il beaucoup?

1. Il parle bien français.

_____

2. Elle gagne beaucoup de compétitions.

_____

3. Il écoute de la musique classique.

_____

4. Elle joue bien au football.

_____

5. Il danse bien.

_____

_____

6. Elle travaille dans une boutique élégante.

_____

K. You are writing your first letter to a French pen pal. Write the questions you ask using **Est-ce que**:

> EXAMPLE: habiter Paris
> Est-ce que tu habites Paris?

1. aimer l'école

_____

2. écouter la musique rock

_____

3. travailler après l'école

_____

4. regarder beaucoup la télévision

_____

5. préparer le dîner

_____

6. marcher à l'école

_____

L. Rewrite the questions in Exercise K using inversion:

1. _____

2. _____

3. _____

4. _____

5. _____

6. _____

M. Form questions using inversion asking what each of the following people are doing now:

Suggestions: regarder la télévision
écouter des disques
jouer au football
marcher à la boutique
travailler à l'hôpital
donner un examen
préparer le dîner
arriver en France
parler au téléphone

EXAMPLE: Georgette regarde-t-elle la télévision?

1. Les filles _____.

2. Le professeur _____.

3. Les docteurs _____.

4. Michelle _____.

5. Thomas _____.

6. Henri et François _____.

7. Maman _____.

8. Lucie et Véronique _____.

____ Leçon 5 _____

A. Express in dollars how much it costs to do each of the following activities:

EXAMPLE: go to the movies ($6.00)   Ça coûte six dollars.

1. buy a slice of pizza ($2.00)   _____

2. buy a hamburger and fries ($5.00)   _____

3. rent a video ($3.00)   _____

4. buy two ice cream cones ($4.00)   _____

5. go to an amusement park ($17.00)   _____

6. buy a compact disk ($12.00)   _____

7. buy three comic books ($8.00)   _____

8. play ten video games ($5.00)   _____

B. Express how many people there are in each family:

EXAMPLE: Les Dupont/17   Il y a dix-sept personnes.

1. Les Martin/15   _____

2. Les Caron/24   _____

3. Les Lesage/9   _____

4. Les Renoir/13   _____

5. Les Dubois/16   _____

6. Les Ricard/3   _____

C. Write the problems from Josette's math book and answer them in French:

    EXAMPLE: $10 + 3 =$ Dix et trois font treize.

1. $12 + 2 =$ _____

2. $30 - 9 =$ _____

3. $20 \div 4 =$ _____

4. $3 \times 8 =$ _____

5. $6 + 5 =$ _____

6. $15 \div 5 =$ _____

7. $27 - 8 =$ _____

8. $7 \times 2 =$ _____

D. Write these Parisian phone numbers in French:

1. 45.13.49.24 _____

2. 48.68.81.92 _____

3. 47.36.16.57 _____

4. 43.75.18.89 _____

5. 46.41.91.26 _____

6. 40.33.67.79 _____

7. 42.52.99.74 _____

8. 49.80.01.44 _____

E. Write out in French how far each student lives from Paris:

    EXAMPLE: Nancy/27 km.   vingt-sept kilomètres

1. Julien/39 km. _____

2. Sylvie/67 km. _____

3. André/90 km. _____

4. Renée/43 km. _____

5. Robert/51 km. _____

6. Lise/83 km. _____

7. Roger/100 km. _____

8. Claire/77 km. _____

F. A French radio announcer is reading off the numbers of the following winning tickets. Write them in French:

1. LOTERIE NATIONALE 10 33 54 _____
_____
_____

2. LOTERIE NATIONALE 17 96 81 _____
_____
_____

3. LOTERIE NATIONALE 75 20 66 _____
_____
_____

4. LOTERIE NATIONALE 41 90 50 _____
_____
_____

5. LOTERIE NATIONALE 15 25 79 _____
_____
_____

6.

```
╔═══════════════════════════╗
║  LOTERIE NATIONALE        ║
║  ┌──────────────────┐     ║
║  │ 88    39     12   │     ║
║  └──────────────────┘     ║
╚═══════════════════════════╝
```

_____

_____

_____

G. Write in French how much each person earns per hour:

EXAMPLE: Marie/100   Marie gagne cent francs l'heure.

1. Christian/66   _____

2. Denise/96   _____

3. Philippe/72   _____

4. Rachel/54   _____

5. Simon/30   _____

6. Charline/84   _____

H. Answer these questions about yourself in French:

1. Combien d'élèves est-ce qu'il y a dans la classe de français?

_____

2. Combien de disques écoutes-tu chaque jour (*each day*)?

_____

3. Combien de programmes de télévision regardes-tu chaque jour?

_____

4. Combien de professeurs aimes-tu?

_____

I. Write a list of the last five things you bought and their prices in French:

1. _____

2. _____

3. _____

4. _____

5. _____

J. Antoine is a teller in a French bank. Express how he would write these dollar amounts the French way:

    EXAMPLE: $2,358.22   2.358,22 dollars

1. $1,746.70 _____

2. $50,800.62 _____

3. $388,217.15 _____

4. $1,525,682.38 _____

K. Label the cost of the following school supplies:

    EXAMPLE: cinq dollars

1. _____

2. _____

3. _____

4. _____

5. _____

6. _____

L. You are planning a party. Write a note in French to a friend. Use numbers to explain your party preparations:

EXAMPLE: Je prépare trois desserts.

_____

_____

_____

_____

____ Leçon 6 _____

A. Roland has an important meeting with a friend. Every few minutes he asks his parents for the time. Write out their responses in French:

EXAMPLE: 7:15   Il est sept heures et quart.

1. 8:30 _____

2. 9:15 _____

3. 10:45 _____

4. 11:20 _____

5. 12:35 _____

6. 1:55 _____

7. 2:05 _____

8. 2:50 _____

B. It's the weekend. Write in French at what time each of these teens wakes up:

EXAMPLE: Anne/7:05   à sept heures cinq

1. Nathalie/6:55 _____

2. Roger/1:15 _____

3. Lisette/10:25 _____

4. Thierry/12:30 _____

5. Claudette/11:35 _____

6. Paul/8:45 _____

7. Liliane/9:10 _____

8. Georges/2:30 _____

C. Write out in French at what time you can see the following shows:

20.30   Fletch aux trousses

Film américain de Michael Ritchie (1986). Durée: 1 h 35. Policier. Rediffusion le 13 octobre 1988.

DISTRIBUTION: Chevy Chase, Joe Don Baker.

L'HISTOIRE - Un riche homme d'affaires propose un marché sordide à Fletch.

22.05   Flash d'informations

22.10   Bobagolfoot
«FOOTBALL»

Présenté par Pierre Sled. Réalisé par Jérôme Revon. Produit par Charles Biétry.

*le match anglais de la semaine (10 mn)*Un match de championnat étranger (10 mn)*Tous les buts de la deuxième division et un match de deuxième division (10 mn)*

22.40   Boxe à Baltard

Commentaires de Jean-Philippe Lustyk et Jean-Claude Bouttier. Réalisé par Jean-Paul Jaud.

Réunion internationale au pavillon Baltard avec notamment: Limarola, Belbouli et Fontana.

0.10   Football américain

(Rediffusion du 9 octobre 1988)

1.05   King Kong II

Film américain de John Guillermin (1986). Durée: 1 h 21. Aventures. Rediffusion le 11 octobre 1988.

DISTRIBUTION: Peter Elliot. Georges Yiasomi.

L'HISTOIRE - Sorti de son coma à la suite d'une opération, King Kong part à la recherche d'un gorille femelle.

---

1. the news

_____

2. a police film

_____

3. a soccer match

_____

4. an adventure film

_____

5. a football game

_____

6. a boxing match

_____

D. Write a list of four things you do during the day and at what time you do them:

1. _____

2. _____

3. _____

4. _____

E. Look at this official French train schedule. Express the departure times in conventional forms:

```
NICE .....................18h19

ANTIBES .................18h40

ST-TROPEZ ...............19h25

CANNES ..................19h58

TOULON ..................20h46

MARSEILLE ...............21h47

AVIGNON .................23h01

VALENCE ................. 0h08

PARIS .................. 0h25
```

EXAMPLE: Nice/18h19
         Nice/à six heures dix-neuf

1. _____

2. _____

3. _____

4. _____

5. _____

6. _____

7. _____

8. _____

F. Express these times as official times:

EXAMPLE: 1:15 p.m.   13h15

1. 2:05 p.m. _____

2. 9:30 p.m. _____

3. 4:35 p.m. _____

4. 6:10 p.m. _____

5. 3:20 p.m. _____

6. 11:00 p.m. _____

7. 12:25 a.m. _____

8. 5:45 p.m. _____

9. 1:35 p.m. _____

10. 7:40 p.m. _____

11. 8:50 p.m. _____

12. 10:55 p.m. _____

_____ Leçon 7 _____

A. Identify in French what Mme Watteau has hanging on her laundry line:

1. _____   5. _____

2. _____   6. _____

3. _____   7. _____

4. _____   8. _____

B. Identify what M. Legrand is packing into his suitcase:

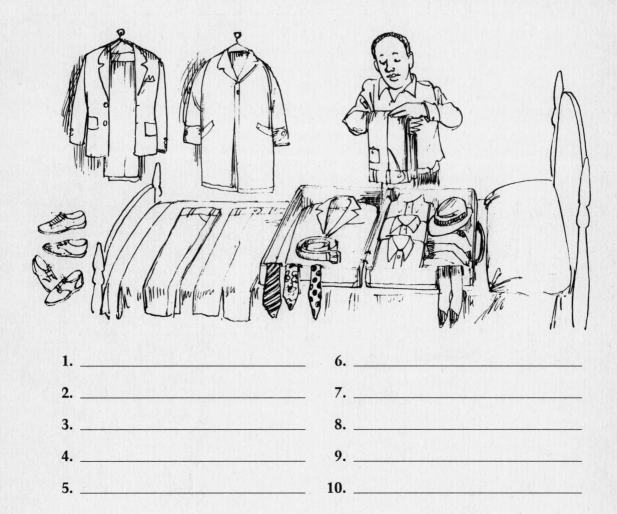

1. _____   6. _____

2. _____   7. _____

3. _____   8. _____

4. _____   9. _____

5. _____   10. _____

C. Use the correct forms of the adjectives to describe the people below:

intelligent	riche	populaire
grand	splendide	fort
charmant	joli	mince
comique	pauvre	formidable

1. Le président est _____.

2. Batman est _____.

3. Le professeur de français est _____.

4. Eddie Murphy est _____.

5. Donald Trump est _____.

6. Arnold Schwartzenegger est _____.

7. Miss America est _____.

8. Raggedy Ann est _____.

9. Cher est _____.

10. Miss Piggy est _____.

D. Write a list of five adjectives in French that describe you:

1. _____   **4.** _____

2. _____   **5.** _____

3. _____

E. Here are some opposites. Can you label them?

1. _____   **2.** _____

3. _____   **4.** _____

5. _____   6. _____

F. Write a list of five new articles of clothing you will buy for next season's wardrobe. Include the colors you prefer:

EXAMPLE: une robe rouge

1. _____

2. _____

3. _____

4. _____

5. _____

G. Describe what new clothes Martine is buying with her birthday money:

EXAMPLE: chemise/petit/noir   une petite chemise noire

1. chaussures/joli/noir   _____

2. pull-over/grand/élégant   _____

3. robe/petit/blanc   _____

4. ceinture/joli/brun   _____

5. chaussettes/petit/bleu   _____

6. manteau/grand/jaune   _____

____ Leçon 8 _____

A. Identify these people in French:

EXAMPLE: C'est une secrétaire.

1. _____

2. _____

3. _____

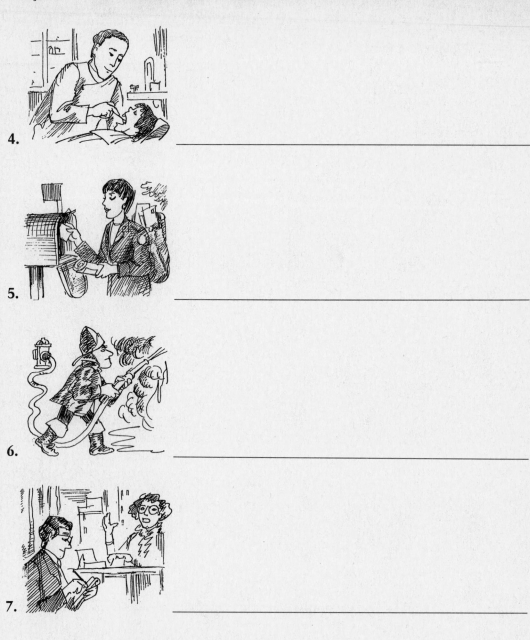

4. _____

5. _____

6. _____

7. _____

8. _____

9. _____

10. _____

B. The people in your class are describing themselves and each other. Express what they say, using the adjectives provided:

aimable	intelligent
sociable	comique
dynamique	intéressant
sincère	formidable

EXAMPLE: Elles sont intelligentes.

1. Tu _____.

2. Nous _____.

3. Geneviève _____.

4. Pierre et Christophe _____.

5. Je _____.

6. Brigitte et Claire _____.

7. Vous _____.

8. Guy _____.

C. Yesterday your friend gave his opinion about some people. Today he is in a bad mood and has completely changed his mind. Rewrite all of his thoughts in the negative:

EXAMPLE: Marc est intelligent.
    Marc n'est pas intelligent.

1. Nous sommes petits.

_____

2. L'actrice est jolie.

_____

3. Les artistes sont pauvres.

_____

4. Je suis mince.

_____

5. L'agent de police est fort.

_____

6. Vous êtes intéressants.

_____

7. Les docteurs sont cruels.

_____

8. Tu es grand.

_____

D. Write a letter in French to your new pen pal asking six questions about him/her:

_____

_____

_____

_____

_____

_____

____ Leçon 9 ____

A. Identify the sports illustrated in the picture:

1. _____   6. _____

2. _____   7. _____

3. _____   8. _____

4. _____   9. _____

5. _____   10. _____

B. You are going to camp this summer and the camp questionnaire asks you to list your four favorite sports. Write your list:

1. _____   3. _____

2. _____   4. _____

C. Fill in the correct form of the verb that makes sense in the sentence. Choose from the following list:

remplir   punir

applaudir   choisir

saisir   finir

1. Vous _____ des joueurs pour l'équipe.

2. Les spectateurs _____ le stade.

3. Je _____ le ballon.

4. _____-tu après le match?

5. Nous _____ le match à quatre heures.

6. L'entraîneur _____ les joueurs qui n'écoutent pas.

D. Write in French what happens in M. Moreau's class:

1. Le professeur/punir/les élèves

_____

2. Jeanne/remplir/le questionnaire

_____

3. Nous/applaudir

_____

4. Vous/saisir/le livre de Jacques

_____

5. Je/finir/tous les exercices

_____

6. Tu/choisir/la réponse correcte

_____

7. Le directeur/applaudir/la classe

_____

8. Nous/choisir/le bon exemple

_____

9. Les garçons/remplir/la liste

_____

10. Vous/finir/le livre

_____

E. Write what happens in this class when M. Moreau is absent by changing all the sentences in Exercise D to the negative:

1. _____

2. _____

3. _____

4. _____

5. _____

6. _____

7. _____

8. _____

9. _____

10. _____

F. Form questions using inversion by asking what each of the following people are doing:

> remplir le stade
> choisir le base-ball
> applaudir les gagnants (*the winners*)
> punir les garçons
> saisir le ballon
> finir le match

1. (elle) _____

2. (l'entraîneur) _____

3. (les filles) _____

4. (tu) _____

5. (vous) _____

6. (ils) _____

G. Form questions using the clues given:

1. (comment) il joue au golf

_____

2. (où) tu pratiques la natation

_____

3. (pourquoi) nous remplissons le stade

_____

4. (quand) vous saisissez la balle

_____

5. (qui) elles punissent

_____

6. (que) je gagne

_____

____ Leçon 10 _____

A. Express what each member of the Ricard family is listening to:

1. M. Ricard écoute _____.

2. Les grands-parents écoutent _____.

3. Henriette écoute _____.

4. Jean et Luc écoutent _____.

5. Maman écoute _____.

6. Les enfants écoutent _____.

B. Fill in the correct form of a verb that makes sense in the sentence, choosing from the following list:

attendre	répondre
entendre	vendre
descendre	

1. Le musicien _____ aux questions.

2. J' _____ le commencement du concert.

3. Nous _____ des disques dans ce magasin.

4. _____-vous la musique?

5. Ils _____ l'escalier.

6. _____-tu la radio?

7. Vous _____ vos amis après le concert.

8. Le magasin _____ des cassettes.

9. Je _____ de l'autobus.

10. Les hommes _____: «oui».

C. Write in French what each person is doing now:

1. tu/attendre Robert

_____

2. nous/descendre du train

_____

3. ils/entendre le transistor

_____

4. vous/répondre à la question

_____

5. je/entendre la fanfare

_____

6. elle/vendre les rafraîchissements (*refreshments*)

_____

D. Show that these activities are not being done by changing all the sentences in Exercise C to the negative.

1. _____

2. _____

3. _____

4. _____

5. _____

6. _____

E. Form questions using inversion asking what each of the indicated subjects is doing. Choose from the following list:

vendre des disques compacts   descendre au magasin
attendre le vendeur   répondre rapidement
entendre le stéréo   vendre des cassettes

1. (elles) _____

2. (le vendeur) _____

3. (ils) _____

4. (tu) _____

5. (vous) _____

6. (Marie) _____

F. Write a list of four musical gifts you could purchase for a family member or friend:

1. _____   **3.** _____

2. _____   **4.** _____

G. Write a composition in French telling about the type of music you like and why:

_____

_____

_____

_____

_____

_____ Leçon 11 _____

A. Complete each sentence with an appropriate part of the body:

1. Je regarde avec _____.

2. J'écoute avec _____.

3. Je touche avec _____.

4. Je travaille avec _____.

5. Je marche avec _____.

6. Je danse avec _____.

7. Je parle avec _____.

8. Je porte le pantalon sur _____.

9. Je porte l'écharpe (*scarf*) sur _____.

10. Je porte le chapeau sur _____.

B. Make sentences by choosing a word or phrase from each group:

J'		les cheveux longs
Marianne	ai	une grande bouche
Vous	ont	les yeux verts
Ils	avons	de longues jambes
Nous	a	une jolie figure
Georges	avez	bon cœur
Tu	as	un long nez
Anne et Cécile		de grandes oreilles

1. _____

2. _____

3. _____

4. _____

5. _____

6. _____

7. _____

8. _____

C. Write a four-sentence note in French to a friend describing your physical appearance:

_____

_____

_____

_____

_____

D. Identify each person's problem:

1. J' _____ .

2. Marie _____ .

3. Tu _____.

4. Nous _____.

5. Ils _____.

6. Vous _____.

E. Say that these people don't have a problem anymore by making each of the sentences in Exercise D negative:

1. _____

2. _____

3. _____

4. _____

5. _____

6. _____

F. You want to find out about some new people you are going to meet. Ask questions about them:

EXAMPLE: René a-t-il de grands pieds?

1. Philippe _____?

2. Les filles _____?

3. Luc et Jean _____?

4. Sylvie _____?

5. Tu _____?

6. Vous _____?

G. Write a list of four physical features you admire in a person:

1. _____

2. _____

3. _____

4. _____

H. These people haven't been entirely honest about their ages. Write out their correct ages in French:

EXAMPLE: (Mme Leblond   56/60)
Mme Leblond n'a pas cinquante-six ans. Elle a soixante ans.

1. (je   15/16) _____

_____

2. (M. Lesage   49/52) _____

_____

3. (vous   27/33) _____

_____

4. (tu   12/13) _____

_____

5. (nous   14/17) _____

_____

6. (M. Tourneau et M. Fournier   73/75) _____

_____

I. Answer these questions about yourself:

1. À quelle heure as-tu faim?

_____

2. Quel âge as-tu?

_____

3. Combien de classes as-tu?

_____

4. Tu as les yeux de quelle couleur?

_____

5. Tu as les cheveux de quelle couleur?

_____

6. Qu'est-ce que tu portes (*wear*) quand tu as froid?

_____

____ Leçon 12 _____

A. Match the animal with the phrase that describes it. Write the matching letter in the space provided:

1. la vache _____
2. le cochon _____
3. l'oiseau _____
4. l'éléphant _____
5. l'âne _____
6. le renard _____
7. le lion _____
8. le chien _____
9. la poule _____
10. le mouton _____

a. Il est stupide.
b. Elle donne des œufs.
c. Elle donne du lait.
d. Il vole (*flies*).
e. C'est le roi (*king*) de la jungle.
f. Il est sale (*dirty*).
g. Il est très rusé (*sly*).
h. Il est grand et gris.
i. Il donne de la laine.
j. C'est le meilleur (*best*) ami de l'homme.

B. You are at the zoo. Tell your friend to do the following:

EXAMPLE: trouver les chiens   Trouve les chiens!

1. regarder les animaux   _____

2. applaudir les singes   _____

3. saisir le lapin _____

4. donner à manger à l'éléphant _____

5. parler au lion _____

6. écouter le tigre _____

7. chercher les oiseaux _____

8. trouver les loups _____

9. admirer le renard _____

10. attendre les chevaux _____

C. Now tell your friend not to do the things in Exercise B by making the commands negative:

EXAMPLE: Ne trouve pas les chiens!

1. _____

2. _____

3. _____

4. _____

5. _____

6. _____

7. _____

8. _____

9. _____

10. _____

D. Mots croisés:

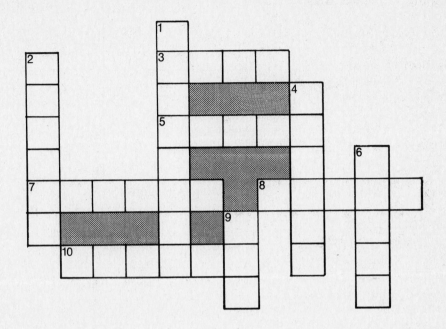

HORIZONTALEMENT
- **3.** lion
- **5.** hen
- **7.** bird
- **8.** cow
- **10.** sheep

VERTICALEMENT
- **1.** elephant
- **2.** pig
- **4.** fox
- **6.** dog
- **9.** donkey

E. Write the advice that M. and Mme Dudard give to their sons:

EXAMPLE: écouter en classe   Écoutez en classe!

1. regarder le tableau   _____

2. écouter le professeur   _____

3. finir les exercices _____

4. répondre aux questions _____

5. choisir les réponses correctes _____

6. attendre la cloche (*bell*) _____ _____

F. Write what the Dudards tell their sons not to do:

    EXAMPLE: parler espagnol   Ne parlez pas espagnol!

1. parler en classe _____

2. attendre vos amis _____

3. punir le professeur _____

4. donner de réponses stupides _____

5. arriver en retard _____

6. applaudir _____

G. Write what suggestions your friends make for today:

    EXAMPLE: regarder la télévision
           Regardons la télévision!

1. travailler au marché

_____

2. jouer au tennis

_____

3. finir nos devoirs

_____

4. écouter la musique classique

_____

5. vendre les disques

_____

6. descendre en ville

_____

H. Your friends have changed their minds. Express the suggestions in Exercise G in the negative:

1. _____

2. _____

3. _____

4. _____

5. _____

6. _____

I. Make a list of four things you want to tell your brother/sister not to do:

1. _____

2. _____

3. _____

4. _____

J. Write a four-sentence note to your parents suggesting what you and your family can do this evening:

_____

_____

_____

_____

_____

___ Leçon 13 _____

A. Tell what the next day is:

1. C'est aujourd'hui mardi.   Demain est _____.

2. C'est aujourd'hui vendredi.   Demain est _____.

3. C'est aujourd'hui lundi.   Demain est _____.

4. C'est aujourd'hui mercredi.   Demain est _____.

5. C'est aujourd'hui dimanche.   Demain est _____.

6. C'est aujourd'hui jeudi.   Demain est _____.

7. C'est aujourd'hui samedi.   Demain est _____.

B. Fill in the missing months:

1. janvier   5. mai   9. _____

2. _____   6. _____   10. _____

3. _____   7. juillet   11. _____

4. _____   8. _____   12. décembre

C. Avant ou après? Give the day that comes before or after the day indicated:

1. le jour avant lundi   _____

2. le jour après dimanche   _____

3. le jour avant vendredi   _____

4. le jour après jeudi   _____

5. le jour avant mercredi   _____

6. le jour après mardi   _____

7. le jour avant dimanche _____

D. Write out in French all the circled dates:

    EXAMPLE: C'est aujourd'hui dimanche, le 6 octobre.

1991

	JANVIER	FÉVRIER	MARS	AVRIL
LUNDI	7 14 21 28	4 11 18 25	4 11 18 25	1 8 15 22 29
MARDI	1 8 15 22 29	5 12 19 26	5 12 19 26	2 9 16 23 30
MERCREDI	2 9 16 23 30	6 13 20 ㉗	6 13 20 27	3 10 17 24
JEUDI	3 10 17 24 ㉛	7 14 21 28	7 14 21 28	4 11 18 25
VENDREDI	4 11 18 25	1 8 15 22	1 ⑧ 15 22 29	5 12 19 26
SAMEDI	5 12 19 26	2 9 16 23	2 9 16 23 30	6 13 20 27
DIMANCHE	6 13 20 27	3 10 17 24	3 10 17 24 31	⑦ 14 21 28

	MAI	JUIN	JUILLET	AOÛT
LUNDI	6 13 20 27	3 ⑩ 17 24	1 8 15 22 29	5 12 19 26
MARDI	7 14 21 28	4 11 18 25	2 9 ⑯ 23 30	6 13 20 27
MERCREDI	1 8 15 22 29	5 12 19 26	3 10 17 24 31	7 14 21 28
JEUDI	2 9 16 23 30	6 13 20 27	4 11 18 25	1 8 15 22 29
VENDREDI	3 10 17 ㉔ 31	7 14 21 28	5 12 19 26	2 9 16 23 30
SAMEDI	4 11 18 25	1 8 15 22 29	6 13 20 27	③ 10 17 24 31
DIMANCHE	5 12 19 26	2 9 16 23 30	7 14 21 28	4 11 18 25

	SEPTEMBRE	OCTOBRE	NOVEMBRE	DÉCEMBRE
LUNDI	2 9 16 23 30	7 14 21 28	4 11 18 25	2 9 16 23 30
MARDI	3 10 ⑰ 24	1 8 15 22 29	5 12 19 26	3 10 17 24 31
MERCREDI	4 11 18 25	2 9 16 23 30	6 13 20 27	4 11 18 ㉕
JEUDI	5 12 19 26	3 10 17 24 31	7 14 21 28	5 12 19 26
VENDREDI	6 13 20 27	4 11 18 25	1 8 15 22 29	6 13 20 27
SAMEDI	7 14 21 28	5 12 19 26	2 9 16 23 30	7 14 21 28
DIMANCHE	1 8 15 22 29	⑥ 13 20 27	3 10 17 24	1 8 15 22 29

1. _____

2. _____

3. _____

4. _____

5. _____

6. _____

7. _____

8. _____

9. _____

10. _____

E. Complete these French sentences:

1. Une année a _____ mois.

2. _____ est le premier (*first*) mois de l'année.

3. _____ est le dernier (*last*) mois de l'année.

4. Le mois de juin a _____ jours.

5. Aujourd'hui est lundi, demain est _____.

6. Aujourd'hui est le premier janvier, demain est _____.

7. Il n'y a pas de classes le samedi et le _____.

8. Les grandes vacances sont en _____ et

   en _____.

9. Le jour de l'Indépendance est le quatre _____.

10. Le jour du Nouvel An est le premier _____.

F. Write out these dates in French:

1. your birthday

_____

2. your parents' birthdays

_____

3. your brother's/sister's birthdays

_____

4. Thanksgiving

_____

5. Easter

_____

6. the first day of school

_____

7. the last day of school

_____

G. A friend you haven't seen in a while would like to see you. Write a note explaining what you do on specific days of this week:

_____

_____

_____

_____

_____

___ Leçon 14 _____

A. What's the weather in the French cities on the map?

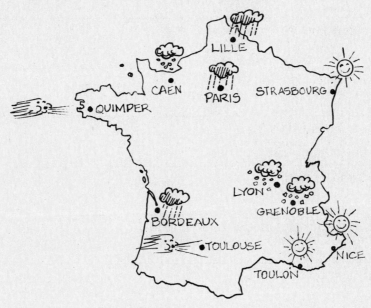

EXAMPLE: À Quimper, il fait du vent.

1. _____

2. _____

3. _____

4. _____

5. _____

6. _____

7. _____

8. _____

9. _____

10. _____

B. Answer the following questions in complete French sentences:

1. Quel temps fait-il en été?

   _____

2. Pendant quels mois fait-il chaud?

   _____

3. Fait-il du soleil à midi?

   _____

4. Quand est-ce qu'il neige?

   _____

5. En quelle saison fait-il froid?

   _____

6. Fait-il très froid en juin?

   _____

7. Quittez (*leave*)-vous la maison quand il pleut?

   _____

8. Quand fait-il du vent?

   _____

9. Que faites-vous quand il fait beau?

   _____

10. Que faites-vous quand il fait mauvais?

   _____

C. Name the season and months for each set of pictures:

1.

   saison _____

   mois _____

   _____

   _____

2.

saison _____

mois _____

_____

_____

3.

saison _____

mois _____

_____

_____

4.

saison _____

mois _____

_____

_____

D. Finish the sentence by expressing in which season you do the following activities:

1. Je fais un pique-nique _____.

2. Je joue au tennis _____.

3. Je joue au football américain _____.

4. Je joue dans la neige _____.

5. Je joue au base-ball _____.

6. Je fais une promenade au parc _____.

7. Je fais un voyage _____.

8. Je fais du ski _____.

E. Create sentences that tell what these people are doing:

Je	faire attention
Marie	faire une partie de base-ball
Nous	faire un voyage
Paul et Jacques	faire une promenade
Tu	faire du ski
Il	faire un pique-nique
Vous	faire les devoirs
Elles	faire une omelette

1. _____

2. _____

3. _____

4. _____

5. _____

6. _____

7. _____

8. _____

F. Express that these people are not doing what they are supposed to be doing:

EXAMPLE: Jean/faire un voyage en Suisse
Jean ne fait pas un voyage en Suisse.

1. Lisette/faire attention

   _____

2. je/faire mes devoirs

   _____

3. ils/faire le dîner

   _____

4. nous/faire la salade

   _____

5. tu/faire la valise (*suitcase*)

   _____

6. vous/faire la liste

   _____

___ Leçon 15 _____

A. M. Leclerc drives a taxi. Express in French where he drops off his customers:

EXAMPLES: au théâtre   à l'hôpital   à la maison

1. _____   2. _____

3. _____   4. _____

5. _____   6. _____

7. _____   **8.** _____

9. _____   **10.** _____

B. Imagine that your French-speaking pen pal comes to visit. List four places he/she might visit in your town:

1. _____   **3.** _____

2. _____   **4.** _____

C. There is a conference at the convention center. Tell from where these people are arriving:

EXAMPLE: Lisette arrive du zoo.

1. M. Savin arrive _____.

2. Mme Lanvin arrive _____.

3. Mlle Constant arrive _____.

4. Liliane arrive _____.

5. Grégoire arrive _____.

6. M. Bernard arrive _____.

7. Mme Bernadot arrive _____.

8. Mlle Nalet arrive _____.

9. Arthur arrive _____.

10. Marthe arrive _____.

11. M. Grévisse arrive _____.

12. Mme Lelong arrive _____.

D. Express what the tourists are talking about:

EXAMPLE: Ils parlent du café.

1. _____

2. _____

3. _____

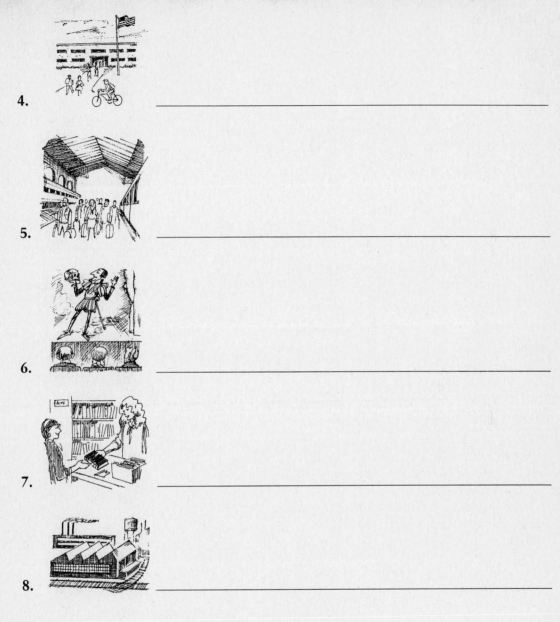

4. _____

5. _____

6. _____

7. _____

8. _____

E. Identify the place in French by combining the elements:

    Example: (café/airport)
            C'est le café de l'aéroport.

  1. (library/school)

_____

2. (factory/family Caron)

_____

3. (apartment/Véronique)

_____

4. (train station/city)

_____

5. (restaurant/hotel)

_____

F. Your Canadian pen pal, Jean, is curious about your town. Answer his questions about it:

Jean: Comment est ta ville?

Vous: _____
      (Say whether it is big or small.)

Jean: Il y a combien d'écoles dans ta ville?

Vous: _____
      (Tell how many there are.)

Jean: Quels sont les cinémas populaires?

Vous: _____
      (Tell what they are.)

Jean: Que fais-tu comme amusement?

Vous: _____
      (Tell what you do.)

Jean: Quel temps fait-il maintenant dans ta ville?

Vous: _____
      (Tell what it is like.)

Leçon 16

A. Andrée has a lot of chores to do today. Express at what time she arrives at each destination:

EXAMPLE: Elle arrive au supermarché à huit heures.

1. _____

2. _____

3. _____

4. _____

5. _____

6. _____

7. _____

8. _____

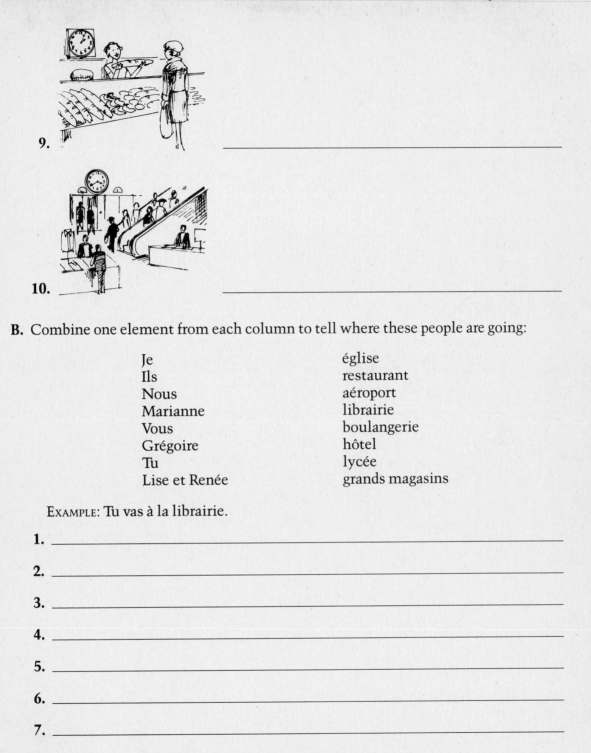

9. _____

10. _____

B. Combine one element from each column to tell where these people are going:

Je	église
Ils	restaurant
Nous	aéroport
Marianne	librairie
Vous	boulangerie
Grégoire	hôtel
Tu	lycée
Lise et Renée	grands magasins

EXAMPLE: Tu vas à la librairie.

1. _____

2. _____

3. _____

4. _____

5. _____

6. _____

7. _____

8. _____

C. Ask if these people are going to the following stores:

    EXAMPLE: Henri/boutique
            Va-t-il à la boutique?

  1. tu/pharmacie

  _____

  2. Pierre/épicerie

  _____

  3. les Caron/boulangerie

  _____

  4. Laure/boucherie

  _____

  5. vous/marché

  _____

  6. Anne et Luc/magasins

  _____

D. Answer all of the questions in Exercise C in the negative:

    EXAMPLE: Il ne va pas à la boutique.

  1. _____

  2. _____

  3. _____

  4. _____

  5. _____

  6. _____

E. List four places that you go to frequently:

  1. _____   **3.** _____

  2. _____   **4.** _____

F. Some stores are closed today. Tell your friend not to go to these places:

EXAMPLE: Ne va pas au magasin!

1. _____

2. _____

3. _____

4. _____

5. _____

6. _____

G. Tell your brother or sister where he/she must go today:

EXAMPLE: Va à la boucherie!

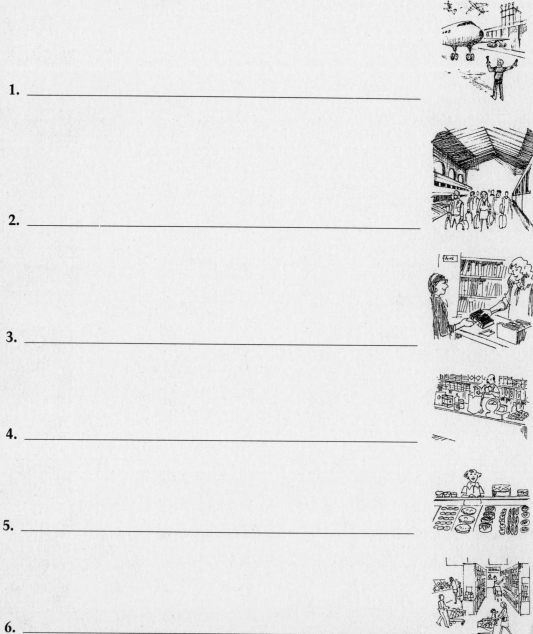

1. _____

2. _____

3. _____

4. _____

5. _____

6. _____

H. Express what these people are going to do in their spare time:

EXAMPLE:

Elle va danser.

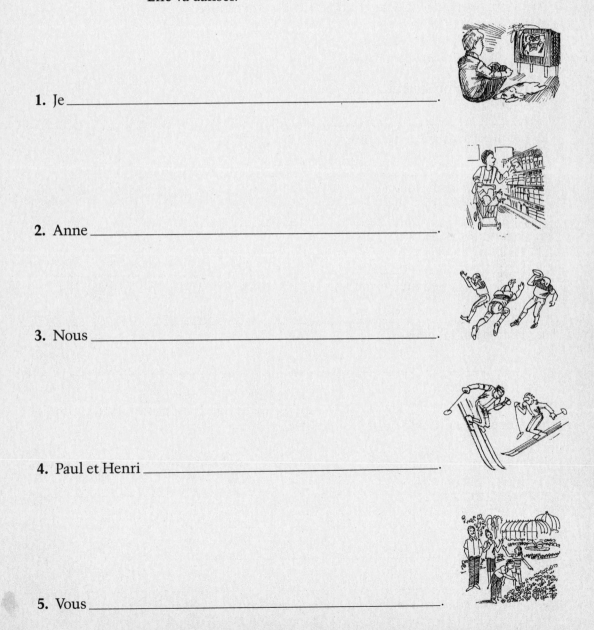

1. Je _____.

2. Anne _____.

3. Nous _____.

4. Paul et Henri _____.

5. Vous _____.

6. Tu _____.

I. Ask if these people are going to do the following things:

EXAMPLE: tu/aller au magasin
Vas-tu aller au magasin?

1. tu/travailler au supermarché

_____

2. Jacques/étudier le vocabulaire

_____

3. elle/aller à la pharmacie

_____

4. vous/finir vos devoirs

_____

5. Marie et Louise/faire l'exercice

_____

6. ils/préparer la mousse

_____

J. Your friend wants to know what you are going to do this summer. Write him/her a four-sentence note explaining your plans:

_____

_____

_____

_____

_____

_____ Leçon 17 _____

A. Here is a plan of the house built by Jacques Laplanche. Identify what you see in the picture:

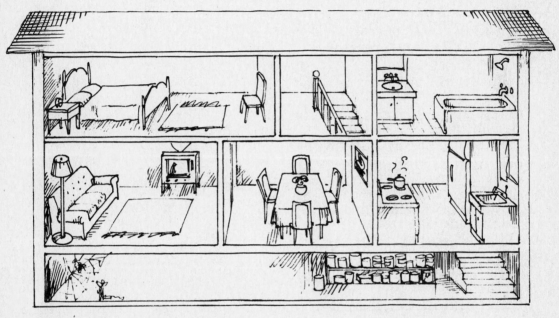

EXAMPLE: C'est la chambre.

1. _____
2. _____
3. _____
4. _____
5. _____

6. _____
7. _____
8. _____
9. _____
10. _____

B. List four items that you have in your bedroom:

1. _____
2. _____

3. _____
4. _____

C. Substitute the French form of the possessive adjective for the definite article:

> EXAMPLE: Il cherche la maison. (our)
> Il cherche notre maison.

1. Les filles regardent les frères. (their)

_____

2. Aimez-vous l'auto? (our)

_____

3. Janine entre dans la chambre. (her)

_____

4. Jean étudie la leçon. (his)

_____

5. Trouves-tu le journal? (my)

_____

6. Ont-ils les crayons? (your, familiar)

_____

7. Nous choisissons les chaussures. (our)

_____

8. Nous invitons les amis à la fête. (your, formal)

_____

9. Finis-tu les devoirs? (your)

_____

10. Il prépare la composition. (his)

_____

D. Change the expressions in bold type to the plural. Make all other necessary changes:

EXAMPLES: Je parle avec **mon ami**.
Je parle avec **mes amis**.

Ma fille est à la plage.
Mes filles sont à la plage.

1. Ma cousine cherche **sa blouse**.

_____

2. Où est **mon frère**?

_____

3. **Notre oncle** est riche.

_____

4. L'élève étudie **sa leçon.**

_____

5. Je ne danse pas avec **son cousin**.

_____

6. As-tu **ton cahier**?

_____

7. **Sa sœur** ne parle pas beaucoup.

_____

8. **Notre professeur** donne beaucoup de devoirs.

_____

9. Fais-tu **ton exercice**?

_____

10. Mon chat n'est pas ici.

_____

E. Rewrite the following phrases, making appropriate changes in the possessive adjectives:

    EXAMPLE: mes frères (famille)
             ma famille

  1. ta maison (livres) _____

  2. nos amis (sœur) _____

  3. votre oncle (cousines) _____

  4. son cahier (crayons) _____

  5. leurs chats (chien) _____

  6. ses chaussures (blouse) _____

  7. notre école (professeurs) _____

  8. ta radio (téléphone) _____

  9. leur divan (chaises) _____

  10. mon problème (devoirs) _____

F. You have just moved to a new house or apartment. Write a note in French to a friend describing your new house:

_____

_____

_____

_____

___ Leçon 18 _____

A. Jeanne is preparing many dishes for a party, and she can't seem to find all the ingredients she needs. Her brother is helping her. Express what he finds:

EXAMPLE: Voici le jambon.

1. _____

2. _____

3. _____

4. _____

5. _____

6. _____

7. _____

8. _____

9. _____

10. _____

11. _____

12. _____

B. List six of your favorite foods:

1. _____   4. _____

2. _____   5. _____

3. _____   6. _____

C. List four foods that you don't like:

1. _____   3. _____

2. _____   4. _____

D. Express what is on the school menu for lunch:

EXAMPLE: Il y a de la viande.

1. _____

2. _____

3. _____

4. _____

5. _____

6. _____

7. _____

8. _____

9. _____

10. _____

11. _____

12. _____

E. You are in a restaurant with your friend Roger, who loves to eat a lot. Express what he says to the waiter:

EXAMPLE: Donnez-moi de la mousse, s'il vous plaît.

1. _____

2. _____

3. _____

4. _____

5. _____

6. _____

7. _____

8. _____

9. _____

10. _____

F. Your local supermarket hasn't had a delivery in a long time. Express what is missing from the shelves:

    EXAMPLE: soupe   Il n'y a pas de soupe.

1. fruits   _____

2. poisson   _____

3. bifteck   _____

4. œufs   _____

5. pain   _____

6. laitue   _____

7. épinards   _____

8. haricots verts _____

9. fromage   _____

10. tomates   _____

G. Your friend has invited you to dinner at his/her house. Write him/her a four-sentence note expressing what you like or don't like to eat:

_____

_____

_____

_____

___ Leçon 19 _____

A. Using the correct form of the verb **vouloir**, tell what everyone wants:

EXAMPLE: je/de l'orangeade
Je veux de l'orangeade.

1. Louis/du thon

_____

2. nous/des œufs durs

_____

3. Marie et Alice/des cerises

_____

4. tu/une fourchette

_____

5. je/des pommes de terre

_____

6. vous/une tasse

_____

7. ils/des saucisses

_____

8. elle/une assiette

_____

9. tu/un sandwich

_____

10. nous/des chips

_____

B. The students in the École Gastronomique are learning to become chefs. Choose one element from each column and state what they can prepare:

Elle	rosbif
Nous	bifteck
Marc et Jean	poisson
Anne	poulet
Je	bouillabaisse
Louise et Micheline	œufs
Tu	salade niçoise
Paul	pommes de terre
Vous	gâteau

EXAMPLE: Elle peut préparer du poulet.

1. _____

2. _____

3. _____

4. _____

5. _____

6. _____

7. _____

8. _____

9. _____

C. Now express that these students can not prepare these dishes by making your answers to Exercise B negative:

EXAMPLE: Elle ne peut pas préparer de poulet.

1. _____

2. _____

3. _____

4. _____

5. _____

6. _____

7. _____

8. _____

9. _____

D. Complete with the proper form of **vouloir**:

1. Je _____ un verre d'eau.

2. _____-vous un sandwich au rosbif?

3. Luc et Pascal _____ mettre le couvert.

4. Nous ne _____ pas d'assiette.

5. Est-ce que tu _____ préparer la salade?

6. Elles ne _____ pas aller au pique-nique.

7. Vous _____ une tasse de café.

8. Je ne _____ pas manger de carottes.

9. _____-tu du gâteau au chocolat?

10. Nous _____ des hot-dogs.

E. Albert is participating in a food-eating contest. Express what he says he can eat by using a form of **tout**:

EXAMPLE: Je peux manger tous les petits pois.

1. _____

2. _____

3. _____

4. _____

5. _____

6. _____

7. _____

8. _____

9. _____

10. _____

____ Leçon 20 _____

A. Fill in the missing letters in each country. Then join the letters to find out where Marie is going for her vacation:

1. H _ ï t i

2. J a p o _

3. E s p a _ n e

4. A l _ e m a g n _

5. É _ a t s-U n i s

6. C h i n _

7. _ u s s i e

8. F _ a n c e

9. I t a l i _

Marie va en _____.

B. From the information on the maps, write the names in French of the following countries:

1. _____

2. _____

3. _____

4. _____

5. _____   6. _____

7. _____   8. _____

9. _____   10. _____

C. By looking at the pictures, tell the nationality of the people mentioned:

1. Luigi est _____.   **2.** Mireille est _____.

3. Dimitri est _____.   **4.** Ces femmes sont _____.

5. Juan est _____.   **6.** Max est _____.

D. You are at an International Youth Congress. All delegates have to write three sentences about themselves and their origins. Express what each person writes:

EXAMPLE: Douglas/Canada/Canadian
Je m'appelle Douglas. Je suis du Canada. Je suis canadien.

1. Mariko/Japan/Japanese

_____

2. Gabrielle/Haiti/Haitian

_____

3. Mario/Italy/Italian

_____

4. Carmen/Spain/Spanish

_____

5. Steve/U.S./American

_____

6. Heidi/Germany/German

_____

7. Janine/France/French

_____

8. Boris/Russia/Russian

_____

E. Describe the nationalities of these students:

> EXAMPLE: Joan/américain
> Joan est américaine.

1. Jean-Paul et Pierre/français

_____

2. Luis et Pablo/espagnol

_____

3. Natasha/russe

_____

4. Victoria/anglais

_____

5. Réginald et Patrick/haïtien

_____

6. Marie-Hélène/canadien

_____

7. Vincenza et Ana Maria/italien

_____

8. Suyin (f.) et HoMing (f.)/chinois

_____

F. A friend of yours is curious about your French cousin. Write a four-sentence note to him/her describing your cousin and his/her background:

_____

_____

_____

_____

___ Leçon 21 _____

A. Tell how these people go to work:

EXAMPLE: Je prends un taxi.

1. Les élèves _____.

2. Nous _____.

3. Marie _____.

4. Le docteur _____.

103

5. Tu _____.

6. Vous _____.

B. Tell where you go to use the following means of transportation:

EXAMPLE: Je vais à l'aéroport.

1. Je vais _____.

2. Je vais _____.

3. Je vais _____.

4. Je vais _____.

5. Je vais _____.

C. Choose one element from each column to tell what means of transportation these people use:

Je		le bateau
Laure	prend	l'avion
Pierre et Luc	prenons	le train
Nous	prennent	le taxi
Les filles	prends	la voiture
Luc	prenez	le scooter
Tu		l'autobus
Vous		la motocyclette

1. _____

2. _____

3. _____

4. _____

5. _____

6. _____

7. _____

8. _____

D. Write what these people are taking for dinner:

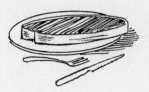

EXAMPLE: Il prend du bifteck.

1. Les garçons _____.

2. Berthe _____.

3. Nous _____.

4. Alain _____.

5. Tu _____.

6. Je _____.

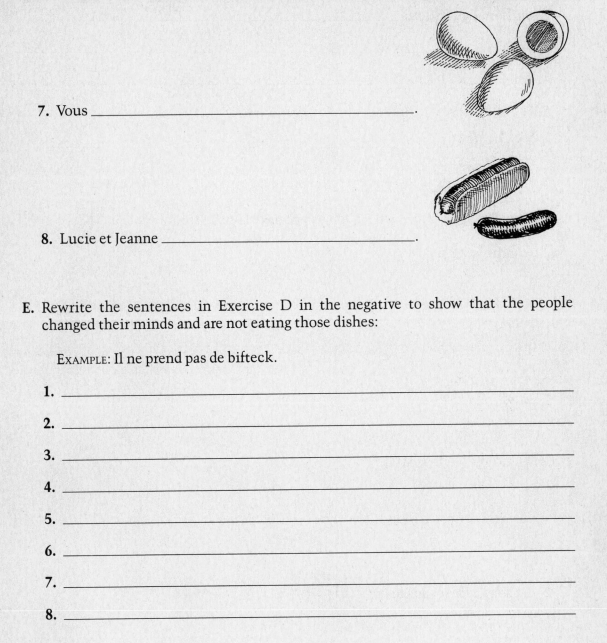

7. Vous _____ .

8. Lucie et Jeanne _____ .

E. Rewrite the sentences in Exercise D in the negative to show that the people changed their minds and are not eating those dishes:

EXAMPLE: Il ne prend pas de bifteck.

1. _____

2. _____

3. _____

4. _____

5. _____

6. _____

7. _____

8. _____

F. Ask if these people understand the following languages:

EXAMPLE: tu/russe   Comprends-tu le russe?

1. vous/anglais _____

2. les hommes/français _____

3. tu/allemand _____

4. Mme Corneille/chinois _____

5. les filles/italien _____

6. Marc/espagnol _____

G. Write a list of six places where you might have left the record you can't find:

EXAMPLE: sous le lit

1. _____   **4.** _____

2. _____   **5.** _____

3. _____   **6.** _____

H. Where is the cat hiding?

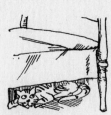

EXAMPLE: Il est sous le lit.

1. _____

2. _____

3. _____

4. _____

5. _____

6. _____

7. _____

8. _____

I. Your friend would like to go to school with you. Explain at what time you leave, how you go to school, with whom you go, and at what time you arrive:

_____

_____

_____

_____

_____

___ Leçon 22 _____

A. There is no school today. Suggest to your friend where you might go:

EXAMPLE: Allons au parc!

1. _____

2. _____

3. _____

4. _____

5. _____

6. _____

7. _____

8. _____

9. _____

10. _____

B. List six places where you would like to go with your best friend on a Sunday afternoon:

1. _____   4. _____

2. _____   5. _____

3. _____   6. _____

C. Tell what each of these people can see from the top of Notre-Dame:

EXAMPLE: il/un jardin
Il voit un jardin.

1. Roger/une église

_____

2. tu/un cirque

_____

3. les garçons/un stade

_____

4. je/un musée

_____

5. Nancy/une piscine

_____

6. vous/un zoo

_____

7. Élise et Carine/une discothèque

_____

8. nous/un théâtre

_____

D. The weather has just changed. Express what these people don't see by changing all the answers in Exercise C to the negative:

EXAMPLE: Il ne voit pas de jardin.

1. _____

2. _____

3. _____

4. _____

5. _____

6. _____

7. _____

8. _____

E. By choosing one element from each column, tell what these people are photographing:

Elle	musée
Je	plage
Paul	matchs
Nous	jardin
Georgette et Lise	surprise-partie
Tu	stade
Les touristes	parc
Vous	piscine
Marie-Thérèse	cirque

EXAMPLE: Elle prend des photos du stade.

1. _____

2. _____

3. _____

4. _____

5. _____

6. _____

7. _____

8. _____

9. _____

F. Some of your friends are talking about their summer plans. Express what they say by being emphatic:

EXAMPLE: Il va aller en Europe.
　　　　　Lui, il va aller en Europe.

1. Il va travailler.

_____

2. Je vais étudier.

_____

3. Elles vont voyager.

_____

4. Tu vas aller en France.

_____

5. Elle va nager à la piscine.

_____

6. Vous allez jouer au tennis.

_____

7. Ils vont faire du cyclisme.

_____

8. Nous allons visiter des amis.

_____

G. Some people can never find anything. Their friends help them out. Complete the sentences:

EXAMPLE: (her) Ton livre est à côté d'**elle**.

1. (us) Ta blouse est chez _____.

2. (you, familiar) Ton cahier est près de _____.

3. (me) Tes disques sont en face de _____.

4. (them m.) Ton frère est derrière _____.

5. (you, formal) Vos cassettes sont devant _____.

6. (him) Ton amie n'est pas loin de _____.

7. (them f.) Ton chien est avec _____.

8. (her) Tes chats vont vers _____.

H. Answer these questions about the students in your class by giving a one-word answer:

    EXAMPLE: (il) Qui danse? **Lui**.

1. (ils) Qui parle français? _____.

2. (elle) Qui choisit la réponse correcte? _____.

3. (je) Qui travaille dur? _____.

4. (nous) Qui fait toujours attention? _____.

5. (elles) Qui ne comprend pas le professeur? _____.

6. (tu) Qui écoute toujours en classe? _____.

7. (il) Qui va fermer la porte? _____.

8. (vous) Qui prépare le dîner? _____.

I. Your friends are discussing what they want to see when they travel in and around Paris:

    EXAMPLE: (I) Jean et **moi**, nous voulons voir la tour Eiffel.

1. (they m.) Roger et _____, ils veulent voir les Invalides.

2. (I) Anne et _____, nous voulons voir le Louvre.

3. (you, familiar) Éric et _____, vous voulez voir Versailles.

4. (she) Lucien et _____, ils veulent voir le Sacré-Cœur.

5. (we) Claude et _____, nous voulons voir Notre-Dame.

6. (he) Pierre et _____, ils veulent voir les Tuileries.

7. (they f.) Lisette et _____, elles veulent voir l'Arc de Triomphe.

8. (you, formal) Christophe et _____, vous voulez voir Montmartre.

___ Leçon 23 _____

A. Robert has won the lottery and is on a shopping spree. Express what items he chooses:

Example:

Il choisit cette télévision à grand écran.

1. _____

2. _____

3. _____

4. _____

5. _____

6. _____

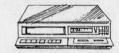

7. _____

8. _____

B. Make a list of five electronic devices you would like to receive as a present:

1. _____

2. _____

3. _____

4. _____

5. _____

C. Annette is having a party and wants her friends' opinions. Finish her questions with the correct form of the demonstrative adjective **ce**, **cette**, **cet**, **ces**:

Que penses-tu de

1. _____ robe?

2. _____ dîner?

3. _____ invitation?

4. _____ décorations?

5. _____ garçon?

6. _____ filles?

7. _____ cassette?

8. _____ chaussures?

9. _____ lecteur de disques compacts?

10. _____ disques?

11. _____ sandwiches?

12. _____ orangeade?

13. _____ magnétoscope?

14. _____ grand écran?

15. _____ téléphone sans fil?

16. _____ fac-similé?

17. _____ four à micro-ondes?

18. _____ caméra vidéo?

19. _____ salade?

20. _____ gâteau?

D. Describe what the customers say about the electronic equipment:

EXAMPLE: four à micro-ondes/moderne
Ce four à micro-ondes est moderne.

1. mini-télévision/excellent

_____

2. lecteur de disques compacts/superbe

_____

3. magnétoscope/extraordinaire

_____

4. machine à écrire électrique/portative

_____

5. calculateur solaire/démodé (*outmoded*)

_____

6. caméra vidéo/populaire

_____

E. Using adjectives that you have learned, write a list of four reasons why you like or dislike a computer:

1. _____

2. _____

3. _____

4. _____

Leçon 24

A. Express what classes these students attend:

EXAMPLE: Pierre

Il est dans la classe de maths.

1. tu

_____

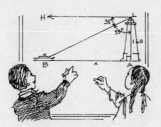

2. Lucie et Anne

_____

3. je

_____

4. nous

_____

5. François et Vincent

_____

6. vous

_____

7. Laure

_____

8. Marcel

_____

B. Tell what each of these people usually receives as a birthday gift:

  EXAMPLE: Lucien/books
         Lucien reçoit des livres.

  1. Liliane/clothes

  _____

  2. je/money

  _____

  3. vous/skates

  _____

  4. Paul et Georgette/records

  _____

  5. nous/shirts

  _____

6. Robert/baseball glove

_____

7. tu/bicycle

_____

8. les filles/cassettes

_____

C. Ask how much money these classmates usually get for their allowance:

EXAMPLE: il/20   Reçoit-il vingt dollars?

1. vous/$18 _____

2. Luc/$10 _____

3. Odette et Pierre/$15 _____

4. Hervé/$13 _____

5. tu/$12 _____

6. Thomas et Richard/$14 _____

D. Tell how these people spent Sunday afternoon:

EXAMPLE: il/étudier   Il a étudié.

1. nous/marcher dans le parc

_____

2. les garçons/jouer au football

_____

3. je/travailler au supermarché

_____

4. Alice/regarder la télévision

_____

5. Régine et Suzanne/écouter des disques

_____

6. tu/garder des enfants

_____

7. Georges/visiter des amis

_____

8. vous/manger au restaurant

_____

E. You went to a party and your parents ask you what you and your friends did there. Write your parents questions:

EXAMPLES: (vous)   Avez-vous dansé?
(Jean)   Jean a-t-il dansé?

1. (Marc) _____

2. (les filles) _____

3. (tu) _____

4. (les garçons) _____

5. (Lise) _____

6. (vous) _____

F. Your friend went to France. Using only the verbs studied in this lesson, write him/her a four-sentence note asking what he/she did while on vacation:

_____

_____

_____

_____

_____